Leopold & Rudolf Blaschka

This book has been made possible by a grant from the Wellcome Trust and was published
to accompany the exhibitions at:

Design Museum, London, 1 March to 30 June 2002

TwoTen Gallery, Wellcome Trust, London, 1 March to 28 June 2002

National Glass Centre, Sunderland, 7 July to 29 September 2002

The Design Museum, the National Glass Centre and the TwoTen Gallery
would like to thank those who have kindly lent to the exhibitions:

Corning Museum of Glass, Corning, New York

Juliette K. and Leonard S. Rakow Research Library of the Corning Museum of Glass, Corning, New York

National Museum & Gallery, Cardiff

Nottingham City Museums & Galleries

We would also like to thank the participating artists:

Christine Borland, Dorothy Cross, Mark Francis, Colin Rennie, Sophie Roët and Samantha Sweet

Special thanks are due to:

Chris Meechan of the National Museum and Gallery, Cardiff, and to Dr Henri Reiling of the
University of Utrecht for their generosity in sharing the fruits of their research into the Blaschkas

We would like to thank the following for their kind permission to use the illustrations
on the pages listed:

National Museum & Gallery, Cardiff: Inside front cover, 29, 31, 32, 33, 34, 35, 36, 37, 41, 42, 43, 44,
52, 53, 57, 58, 59, inside back cover

Juliette K. and Leonard S. Rakow Research Library of The Corning Museum of Glass, Corning,
New York: 2, 3, 8, 11, 30, 40, 54, 56

Cornell University: 49

Frieze Magazine (photographer, James Harris): 38, 39, 45, 50, 51, 55, 60, back cover

Nottingham City Museums & Galleries: Front cover, 18, 24, 46, 47, 48

ISBN 1-872005-45-4

Edited by James Peto and Angie Hudson

Designed by Joe Ewart and Niall Sweeney for Society

Printed by Futura Printing, London

© 2002 Design Museum, National Glass Centre, TwoTen Gallery and the authors

Contents

Foreword

Beneath the superficial beauty of *Aequorea victoria*, one of the sea creatures represented in glass by Rudolph and Leopold Blaschka, lie some contentious issues for contemporary biomedicine. This limpid, undulating jellyfish is sought after for its green-fluorescent protein (GFP). Sequenced, cloned and expressed as a cellular marker, GFP allows scientists to see at a glance whether an attempt to introduce a gene into an organism has been successful. The medical and environmental benefits derived from GFP are potentially enormous.

The artist Christine Borland's video work 'The Aether Sea', shown as part of the TwoTen Gallery's Blaschka exhibition, was created following her research fellowship at the Medical Research Council's Social & Public Health Sciences Unit at Glasgow University. Katrina Brown, in her essay on Borland's installation for the publication 'Progressive Disorder', says 'The Aether Sea' pays tribute to these creatures -"the humble life form that has given birth to one of the most revolutionary and invaluable technologies." But what of the ethical implications of GFP? The 'green gene' has already been used as a marker in mammals reared for potential xenotransplantation, and is known more widely through media coverage of 'Alba', the green-glowing, transgenic rabbit-cum-artwork by the Chicago-based artist Eduardo Kac. Is 'Alba' medical miracle or artistic chimera?

Issues that are important to the Glasgow unit in which Borland worked, such as examining the sociological and ethical implications of advances in medical genetics, are being investigated by academic researchers supported by the Wellcome Trust under its BioMedical Ethics Programme. They are also investigated in other ways through exhibitions at the Trust's TwoTen Gallery. Examining topical social issues through historical and contemporary exhibitions is part of the Trust's commitment to public engagement with science. We are therefore pleased to be in partnership

Denna Jones
Curator, TwoTen Gallery & Contemporary Initiatives
The Wellcome Trust

with the Design Museum and the National Glass Centre, both as sponsor of this publication and as a satellite exhibition venue. By reaching a new audience through this exhibition, we hope to provide a catalyst for continuing biomedical discussion and debate.

James Peto, Curator, Design Museum
Ann Jones, Associate Curator, National Glass Centre

During the 1880s the small Dresden workshop run by the father and son partnership of Leopold and Rudolf Blaschka experienced a major shift in its sales. At the beginning of the decade its chief source of income had been costume jewellery and the supply of glass eyes to taxidermists and to the blind. But, by 1889, orders for the exquisite glass models of invertebrate sea creatures, which the Blaschkas had first begun to make in 1863, started coming in at such a rate that before long they were struggling to keep pace with the demand.

The Blaschkas had inadvertently discovered a market which expanded until they were keeping salesmen busy across Europe and the United States and attracting orders from as far afield as Japan and India. This curious demand for sea anemones, jellyfish and other invertebrates modelled in glass was fuelled by a growing thirst for scientific knowledge and by the late 19th century fascination with the exotic and the hitherto unknown. Teeth-baring tigers and brightly plumed birds from far-flung corners of the Empire could be photographed or hunted down, stuffed and then mounted in elaborate dioramas to satisfy the curiosity of the increasing numbers of visitors to our municipal museums. The world beneath the waves was a different matter. This was long before Jacques Cousteau perfected the acqualung and full-colour underwater photography, and – until the Blaschkas – there was no way to capture the extraordinary translucent forms and vibrant colours that marine biologists were discovering in the world of undersea invertebrates.

By 1888 the Blaschkas' sales catalogue listed models of up to 700 different sea creatures. As early as 1865 the Natural History Society of Northumberland, Durham and Newcastle upon Tyne had acquired a large group and soon there were prized collections of Blaschka models in national and municipal museums up and down Britain. However, by the last

third of the 20th century most of these collections had been relegated to half-forgotten storage cupboards. The rapid advance of science and the development of film and photography had revealed them to be sometimes inaccurate (unsurprising, since many were copied from book illustrations rather than from life). Furthermore, in an age of synthetic materials, glass as a medium for modelling seemed somehow antiquated.

This book and the exhibitions it accompanies offer an opportunity to bring them back into the light, repair their broken tentacles and re-examine them - for their intrinsic beauty, for their technical virtuosity and for their testimony to an extraordinary period of scientific exploration and museological history.

Described by a contemporary as an 'an artistic marvel in the field of science and a scientific marvel in the field of art', Blaschka models were sold primarily as aids to education in the natural sciences. However, Leopold Blaschka also advertised his creations as 'ornaments', realising their potential as 'decorations for elegant rooms'. A Blaschka anemone, squid or jellyfish remains difficult to categorise. These glass creatures do not fit comfortably into any of the conventional pigeonholes of science, art, craft or design, but seem to have at least one tentacle in each of them. It seems appropriate, therefore, that the exhibition of the Blaschkas' work will be seen in a range of institutions - each of which has a different focus, but which between them cover all the above fields.

We would like to thank all those who have lent to the exhibition and contributed to this publication. We are especially indebted to Chris Meechan of the National Museum & Gallery, Cardiff, for his generosity in sharing with us the fruits of his research into the Blaschkas, as well as to Dr. Henri Reiling of the University of Utrecht and to the living artists whose work has expanded the scope of the exhibition.

Leopold and Rudolf Blashka
and natural history in the 19th century

The second half of the 19th century was a time of great scientific discovery. New museums were being built throughout the world and many existing private museums were opening to the public. New galleries were designed to display the expanding array of known living plants and animals. For many groups of animals this was easily done: birds, mammals, reptiles and even fish could be skinned and mounted to produce reasonably accurate and lifelike representations. Insects, with their hard exoskeletons, could simply be dried and then pinned to boards for study or display.

But what about soft-bodied animals such as jellyfish and sea anemones? Examples of these animals could be pickled in spirit to preserve them, but this in no way reflected their extraordinary appearance in life. Their colours quickly faded and their shapes became distorted as the tissues shrank. Papier-mâché and wax models could not capture their translucence and transparency. Leopold Blaschka, a brilliant glassworker and amateur naturalist, devised a solution to this problem - vividly recreating these life forms by modelling them in glass.

Leopold Blaschka came from a long line of glassworkers. As far back as the 15th century a Blaschka was registered in Prague as an artificer in decorative glass. For a time the family lived in northern Austria and then Bohemia, now in the Czech Republic, where Leopold's grandfather owned a sawmill and a glass furnace. His second son Joseph, Leopold's father, moved to Aicha in northern Bohemia, and it was here that Leopold was born on 27th May 1822, the youngest of three sons.

Leopold showed an early aptitude for painting and it was suggested that he should study art in Vienna and Italy. However, his father wanted him to undergo a more practical training. He was therefore apprenticed for a year in a merchant's store before joining his brother for instruction in working with precious metals and cutting gemstones. Some years later he

Chris Meechan, National Museum & Gallery, Cardiff
Dr. Henri Reiling, University of Utrecht

began working with his father to learn the traditional family metal and glass-working skills.

Leopold was married in 1846 to the daughter of a local mill owner, but his wife died during a cholera epidemic four years into the marriage. Depressed and in poor health Leopold led a reclusive existence until, encouraged by a local doctor who owned a substantial library of natural history books, he began to study and to paint plant-life. Gradually he recovered his health, but following the death of his father in 1852 he felt the need to get away and early in 1853 he left for America. During the voyage his ship was becalmed for two weeks, allowing Leopold time to trawl for and make drawings of jellyfish. This was his first opportunity to study from life creatures he had previously known only from illustrations, and which were to play such an important role in his future career.

On reaching America he remained for some months in New York where he entered into business supplying goods to a number of wholesale jewellery firms. He returned home to Aicha in the winter of the same year. In 1854 he married Carolina Riegel and established a glass workshop in his father-in-law's house, where his position as supervisor of several workmen allowed him plenty of time to pursue his botanical studies.

Leopold's son Rudolf was born on 17th June 1857. It was around this time that Leopold began experimenting with making artificial flowers in glass - principally as an exercise to demonstrate his skill. He is unlikely to have realised that these models would eventually lead to a life dedicated to natural history.

His first botanical creations were based on the orchids in the greenhouses of Prince Camille de Rohan, an enthusiastic connoisseur and collector of plants. On his estate at Sychrov Castle, Bohemia, the Prince

had laid out a world-famous garden, reflecting the 19th century fascination with botany, then a science offering constant new discoveries.

Between 1860 and 1862 Leopold constructed a series of some 100 models representing nearly fifty species of these exotic specimens - principally as an exercise to demonstrate his craftsmanship. The Prince introduced Leopold to Professor Ludwig Reichenbach, the Director of the Royal Natural History Museum and Botanical Garden in Dresden, and as a result he was invited to display the orchid models in the pavilion of the Botanical Garden in the summer of 1863. Although they were much admired for their beauty and craftsmanship they aroused little commercial interest.

As a result of the exhibition, however, an Englishman living in Dresden suggested to Leopold that he make a set of models of sea anemones in glass as these creatures were so difficult to preserve. For reference he lent a copy of, 'Actinologia Britannica: A History of British Sea Anemones and Corals' which had recently been published by the influential naturalist, Philip Henry Gosse. The illustrations in this book were to provide the principal source material for the early marine models.

It was Gosse who inspired the British craze for aquaria which began around the middle of the 19th century when cheap plate glass first became available. This, combined with the discovery that animals could be kept alive in water oxygenated by seaweed, led to the introduction of aquaria into many of the most fashionable drawing rooms. The seawater aquarium was first mentioned in Gosse's 'A Naturalist's Wanders on the Devonshire Coast' - another important source book for Leopold. Much later, inspired by Gosse's idea, the Blaschkas were to install an aquarium in their own studio.

Professor Reichenbach subsequently purchased the set of anemone models for the Dresden Museum. Exhibited in artificial aquaria, they came

to the attention of curators from other natural history museums across Europe. Leopold began supplying sets of anemones to such museums as well as to a growing number of private collectors.

The first sets of models comprised sixty-eight sea anemones mounted on plaster bases painted to resemble rock. After this, Leopold expanded his catalogue, with the majority of models consisting of three-dimensional glass interpretations of zoological illustrations. Little commercial or scientific interest seems to have been shown in the early models. This is borne out by the fact that anatomical errors in their designs were not corrected for some time after they were first publicised in the catalogues. For instance, a model that represented a single tentacle was offered as a model of a complete sea anemone. Other anemones were presented as almost flat discs showing the mouth only, which faithfully reflected the original illustrations. Because these had been drawn from above, the body that supported the mouth was not visible - and so it had been omitted from the models.

Such mistakes demonstrate the innate difficulty of copying from two-dimensional source material, however accurate that material might be. A picture emerges of Leopold studying on his own, painstakingly recreating biological illustrations, but without direct contact with the naturalists who had first-hand experience of the creatures he was modelling.

The initial anemone models came to be supplemented by rather less decorative creatures - such as worms, echinoderms, molluscs and jellyfish. In the preface to Leopold's early catalogue of 1871 (which offered nearly 300 different models) Reichenbach recommended the glass models as being very true to nature. Reichenbach also influenced the Blaschkas' selection of subjects. From a letter by Rudolf Blaschka to the director of the

Botanical Museum of Harvard University, we know that Reichenbach occasionally brought along snails that he had found on his excursions and asked to have models made of them for the museum. On another occasion he referred to figures in an old book "from the former century" (i.e. the 18th) and ordered models of the animals it depicted.

To begin with the business did not pay well, perhaps due to the low pricing of the models. Assisted by Rudolf, Leopold was obliged to concentrate on other sources of income, producing decorative items of jewellery, such as brooches, fans, and earrings. The Blaschkas also made and sold glass eyes - mostly for cosmetic use by the blind but also for taxidermists. This enterprise resulted by chance after Leopold had heard people complaining about the fragility of artificial eyes made in Paris. He prepared some eyes from solid 'glass-mass' which, though they were never advertised, became widely sought after. Despite the fact that neither of them took any pleasure in modelling the eyes, the Blaschkas' workshop carried a large stock and it was not until they moved out of Dresden to nearby Hosterwitz in 1887 that they ceased to make them.

From 1866 onwards the business received modest orders for models each year. In 1876 an order for two complete collections of models from the South Kensington Museum, London, (now the Natural History Museum) provided a significant boost. It helped inspire Leopold's son, Rudolf, to further his studies of zoology and anatomy and to immerse himself in the great natural history library of the Imperial Academy Leopoldina in Dresden. Here both father and son studied illustrated books and copied many of the drawings as sources of reference for the glass animals. Hundreds of their reference drawings survive and are today housed in the Rakow Library at the Corning Museum of Glass, Corning, New York.

In 1876, at the age of nineteen, Rudolf Blaschka joined his father

full-time in the glassworkers' studio. This fresh blood seemed to revive and add new flair to the business. In 1877 contact was made with Professor Ernst Haeckel, a prominent zoologist at the University of Jena. Professor Haeckel lent the Blaschkas books from his library so that they could copy the illustrations. The Blaschkas maintained an important professional friendship with him, and it is likely that they visited each other.

Haeckel had a highly productive scientific career. He created more than 2,000 genus names and described more than 3,500 species. He was also open to new ideas, applying Charles Darwin's theory of evolution (published in 1859) to the science of systematics as early as 1862. He believed that related animal groups illustrated different stages of evolutionary development: Haeckel's 'Biogenetic Law' claimed that a species' embryonic development reflected its evolutionary development. This law elaborated on ideas about embryonic development first explored in Germany as part of the 19th century trend in biological thinking known as 'Naturphilosophie'. Naturphilosophie opposed the rationalism of the Enlightenment and saw the universe as a dynamic, developing organism rather than as a regulated machine. It sought harmonies and parallels in nature and stimulated research into embryology and comparative morphology.

Several of Haeckel's publications were used as preparatory material by the Blaschkas. Typical features of the illustrations, such as symmetry and undulating shapes, are reflected in their models. This could be interpreted as a parallel development, but it is likely that the Blaschkas were directly influenced. Haeckel's commitment to the decorative arts culminated in the publication of his 'Kunstformen der Natur' [Artforms in Nature] (1899-1904), a work considered to have influenced the development of the decorative style based on

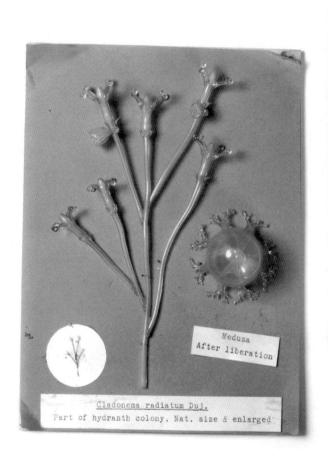

Cladonema radiatum (part of hydranth colony, natural size and enlarged)
Medusa (the floating sexual phase of the life cycle)

Medusa
After liberation

Cladonema radiatum Duj.
Part of hydranth colony. Nat. size & enlarged

18

organic forms known as 'Jugendstil', the German version of Art Nouveau.

In 1877, the year that the Blaschkas made contact with Haeckel, Leopold ordered two shipments of specimens preserved in alcohol from the zoological station at Naples so that he could compare them with his own preparatory drawings, carefully copied from zoological illustrations. This is the earliest known example of the Blaschkas actually seeing the animals that they portrayed in glass (albeit in a preserved state). The zoological station at Naples was the first marine research station in the world. It was founded in the early 1870s by Anton Dohrn, one of Haeckel's students, and became a magnet for naturalists throughout Europe who were eager to see living specimens of the extraordinary marine life forms that were being discovered.

Leopold intended to publish a new catalogue of the studio's models. This probably appeared in 1878, but no copy survives. What has survived is the North American sales catalogue from that year. Leopold wrote to Haeckel that the new catalogue was intended to be scientific. An analysis of the collection on offer suggests that the majority of models were still based on published zoological illustrations.

However, within this framework, new themes can be noted. For the first time series of models were offered which represented stages of embryonic development rather than just the adult life form. Possibly these were inspired by the ideas explored in Haeckel's 'Biogenetic Law'. In addition, anatomical models of different animal groups were offered for sale, reflecting the contemporary enthusiasm for comparative morphology.

The Blaschkas' later glass models were intended to function as scientific exhibits and teaching aids rather than as decorative items. The printed materials on which they were based were considered to be scientifically authoritative. Therefore only by closely replicating this source could the glass models themselves be considered scientifically valid.

Observations on real and living animals increased the accuracy of the later models. In 1879 Rudolf went on a field trip to northern Italy and the Adriatic and it was around this time that seawater aquaria were installed in the Blaschkas' Dresden studio. To stock them, living marine animals were supplied by the zoological station at Trieste, Italy, and also by the British trader R.T. Smith of Weymouth.

Only a small proportion of the modelled species, less than an estimated ten per cent, can be assumed to have resulted from actual contact with the animals. Yet such contact must have had an important influence on the Blaschkas' development as model makers, offering an opportunity for close examination, deepening their understanding of morphology and leading to better representations of the animal body in glass.

Nineteenth-century scientists showed an almost insatiable desire to discover and describe the natural world. Colonialism in particular had opened up entire continents for exploration and study. The findings of these numerous scientific expeditions were published with descriptions and illustrations of newly discovered animal and plant species. The Blaschkas made use of these reports when seeking ideas for new additions to their catalogue. With such inclusions their collections began to acquire an exotic aspect. Descriptions of molluscs and echinoderms from the archipelago of the Philippines; coral animals from the Red Sea; molluscs from Polynesia and siphonophores from Lanzarote were all eagerly copied as valuable source material.

The voyage of the British ship 'Challenger', the first worldwide oceanographic expedition, was particularly widely reported. Samples of animals found during the expedition were sent to specialists everywhere to analyse and describe. The voyage of the 'Challenger' left

its traces in the Blaschkas' oeuvre as well - in their remarkably complex glass models of sponges found by the expedition.

The models were commissioned by Professor Franz Eilhard Schulze of Berlin, in 1885, and were based on illustrations of Schulze's research and his own microscope slides. Schulze himself made suggestions for improvements to the models and Leopold subsequently made the required alterations. This co-operation continued with the production of models showing enlargements of sections of sponge tissue and spiculae.

The 'Challenger' models were completed in 1886 and Schulze was immensely proud of them. Prior to this the Blaschkas had kept in touch with science primarily through printed materials, so this direct contact with an experienced naturalist and the opportunity to incorporate feedback from Schulze into their work marked a new stage in their scientific model-making career.

Comparison between early and later models by the Blaschkas reveals a tendency towards increased scientific accuracy and away from the more showy style of the "decorations for elegant rooms", as the models were described in the first catalogues. The Blaschkas were keen to accommodate customer demand for the glass models of sea animals and continued to expand their range accordingly. By 1888 the catalogue published by Henry Ward, their agent in the United States, listed 700 models.

The models varied greatly in complexity and in their method of construction. Component parts were formed from both clear and coloured glass using a combination of glass-blowing and lamp-working techniques. The parts were then either directly fused together or assembled with adhesives - probably animal glues. Where necessary other materials were used in the construction. Fine copper wires were

added to reinforce or attach delicate tentacles and gills and painted paper was cleverly incorporated to represent internal structures.

Ingeniously, the Blaschkas also made use of the actual shells of terrestrial, freshwater and marine gastropods and introduced a series in which modelled glass bodies were attached to the shells of bivalve molluscs. A series of anatomical models was also produced – almost certainly based on their own dissections of specimens.

Great attention was paid to achieving the correct appearance of the living animals. A fine speckled layer of pigment, often applied to the inner surface of the glass, conveyed a jelly-like translucence. Where thicker skin or a textured appearance was required the paint or enamel was applied in deeper coats often mixed with a fine 'granular' material - possibly fused, powdered glass.

Many Blaschka models found their way to the Museum of Comparative Zoology at Harvard and it was here that Professor George Lincoln Goodale, who was planning the new galleries in the adjacent Botanical Museum, first saw them. Convinced that glass would be the ideal medium in which to fashion plant models, he visited the Blaschkas in their Dresden studio in 1886. He persuaded them to make some sample flowers and subsequently commissioned them to produce models of plants on a half-time contract.

It was a pity for the future of the glass models of marine creatures that this offer was made at precisely the same time as they were making such advances in the scientific accuracy of their models. The production of the botanical models came to take up more and more of their time.

By 1890 the Blaschkas decided that they no longer wished to divide their time between the plant and animal models. They were offered an exclusive, ten-year contract with Harvard and work on the animals came to

a halt. Leopold died in 1895 at the age of 73. By the time of Rudolf's death the botanical collection consisted of some 847 life-size model plants, and over 3,000 enlarged flowers and anatomical sections. Periodically renewing the Harvard contract, Rudolf continued the work on his own right up until 1936. He died three years after he finally ceased work on the flowers at the age of 82.

While the flowers remain a highly valued part of the collections of the Botanical Museum, Harvard, and the Corning Museum of Glass, the collections of glass animals have not been so fortunate. Many are either lost or, because of changing fashions, removed from display. It is hoped that this publication and the accompanying exhibitions will help to rekindle interest in these curious and irreplaceable creations.

Medusae
All Things Bright and Beautiful

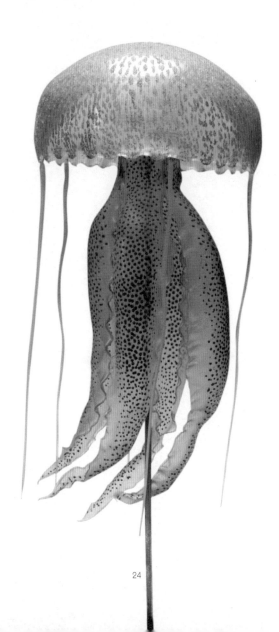

Pelagia noctiluca (jellyfish)

Dorothy Cross

Jellyfish (*medusae*) are composed of 98 per cent water. They are exquisite creatures of fragility and grace, yet some species contain a venom that is amongst the most fatal known on earth. We cannot view their true form outside their natural realm, so most humans encounter these animals only as viscous blobs washed up on the shoreline during the summer months.

Jellyfish evolved early in earth's history and have continued on a clear, separate, evolutionary pathway. They are a loose assemblage of cells, efficient and mysterious. There is much still to learn about these animals. It is probable that undiscovered species outnumber those already known to us. Their biomass remains unmeasured in the oceans. They defy most gathering processes, their jellied body structure breaking apart when caught in nets. Certain species of *cubo-medusae* have eyes but they do not have a brain. Yet to view their eyes under a microscope is like looking at our own.

In the middle of the 19th century the membrane of the ocean's surface was only just beginning to be penetrated. Among its mysterious denizens, jellyfish, in particular, held a fascination for both professional and amateur naturalists. In Dresden, Germany, Leopold and Rudolf Blaschka devised ways to model jellyfish and other marine invertebrates in molten glass. On Valentia Island, off the extreme south-west tip of Ireland, Maude Delap gathered *medusae* and succeeded in breeding them in captivity. In Jena, Germany, the Darwinist zoologist, Ernst Haeckel, lived in a house named Villa Medusa.

During their lifetimes the Blaschkas produced thousands of marine and botanic specimens in glass. Originally renowned for their marine invertebrates, they also created the famous collection of glass flowers commissioned by the Botanical Museum at Harvard. By the time the contract ended they had produced hundreds of specimens - each cactus spine and flower sepal exquisitely fragile. Packed in straw in cardboard

boxes they were transported to the United States, travelling from the port of entry by hearse, the least turbulent means of road transport. But it was their invertebrate models which were in worldwide demand, and several excellent pieces were acquired by the Natural History Museum in Dublin, where they would have been seen by Maude Delap.

Delap was born in Donegal, Ireland, in 1866, the daughter of a Church of Ireland minister. She was one of nine children, all encouraged to be avid naturalists. When her family moved to the island of Valentia in County Kerry when Maude was six, she turned her eyes towards the sea. She ventured out daily in her punt collecting unusual specimens and dragnetting for plankton to feed her jellyfish. Maude received invitations to continue her studies outside Ireland but was refused permission to travel by her father who would not let any unmarried daughter of his leave the home. However, at an early age she entered into a correspondence with the Natural History Museum in Dublin that continued until a few years before her death in 1953. Maude Delap was the first person to breed jellyfish in captivity. Working without any technical assistance she placed the budding jellyfish in bell jars in her father's house and documented the development of *Cyanea lamarcki* and *Chrysaora isosceles* through to adulthood.

At the same time, Professor Ernst Haeckel was carrying out his studies at Jena University. As a young zoologist he had travelled extensively, searching shore and ocean for undiscovered specimens. He was the author of the superbly illustrated book 'Kunstformen der Natur' [Artforms in Nature]. Haeckel, too, had an abiding passion for jellyfish. At the Villa Medusa he lived in rooms with jellyfish patterns painted on the ceilings, drank from porcelain teacups patterned with jellyfish and ate off tablemats embroidered with *Rhizostomae* at a table decorated with inlaid undersea

creatures. His first wife died after a year of marriage. Broken-hearted he named a particularly beautiful jellyfish after her: *Desmonema Annasethe*.

Haeckel's work was of great importance to the Blaschkas, with whom he corresponded, though it is not certain that they ever have met. Maude Delap saw the Blaschkas' models in the Natural History Museum in Dublin but, although he travelled to Dublin in 1906 en route to Scotland to lecture, Maude Delap never met Haeckel.

There was no sub-aqua gear available to Maude Delap. To watch underwater life she used a megaphone-shaped viewer held to the surface of the sea. For many years the Blaschkas, living in land-locked Saxony, had no access to the creatures they were attempting to model accurately in glass. They had to work from other people's drawings. Nineteenth century communications were difficult and travel was slow. Nevertheless, such constraints, allied to the fertility of the Victorian imagination and its thirst for wonder, only served to heighten the curiosity of the turn-of-the-century naturalist and to stimulate further scientific research.

Today scientists are constrained by institutional funding. The purpose of their research is often to prove rather than to discover. For Ernst Haeckel, Maude Delap and the Blaschkas the excitement of discovery was a daily possibility.

Works

Actineria hemprichi (sea anemone)

Large group of **Actinoloba dianthus** (sea anemones) showing varieties, forms and growth stages

A Blaschka drawing of sea anemones based on the illustrations of P.H.Gosse

Spongodes celosia (soft coral)

Carinaria mediterranea (pelagic gastropod)

37

Sabellaria alveolata (polychaete worm)

Terebella emmalina (marine worm)

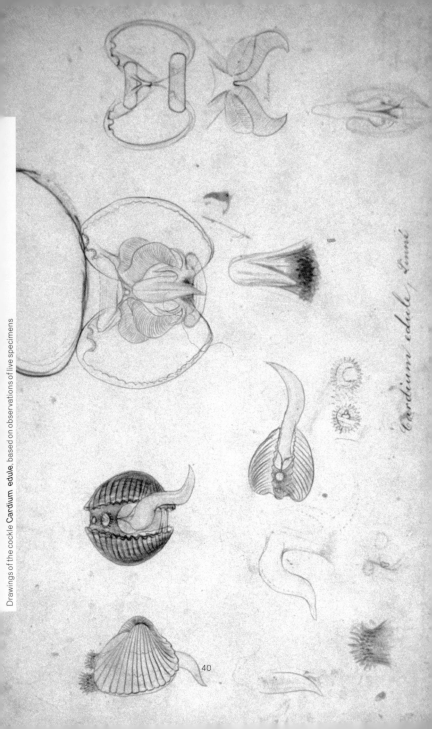

Cardium edule, Linné

40

The cockle, **Cardium edule**, with a glass body glued to a real shell

Doliolum mülleri (planktonic tunicate) greatly enlarged

42

44

Aurelia aurita (common Moon jellyfish)

46

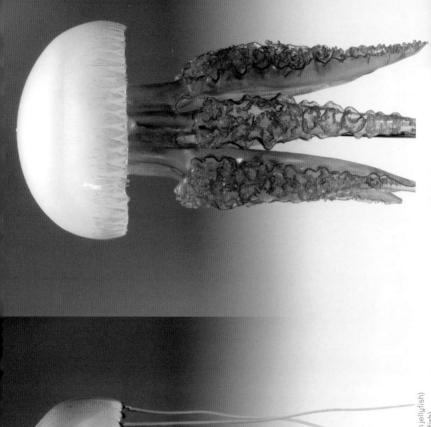

47

Chrysaora hysocella (Scyphozoan jellyfish)
Cyanhasaa tani (Scyphozoan jellyfish)

Aurelia aurita
Nr. 225.

Eight stages in the development of the common jellyfish, with updated shapes

49

Rhizostoma pulmo (jellyfish) model and pickled specimen

Spirit 294

48

Comatula hamata (feather starfish)

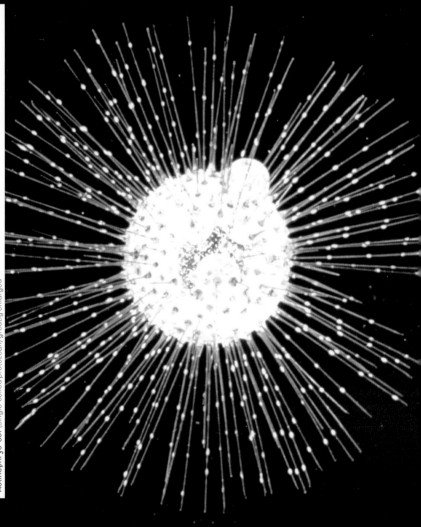

Actinophrys sol (single-celled protozoan) greatly enlarged

Heliosphaera actinota (single-celled protozoan) greatly enlarged

53

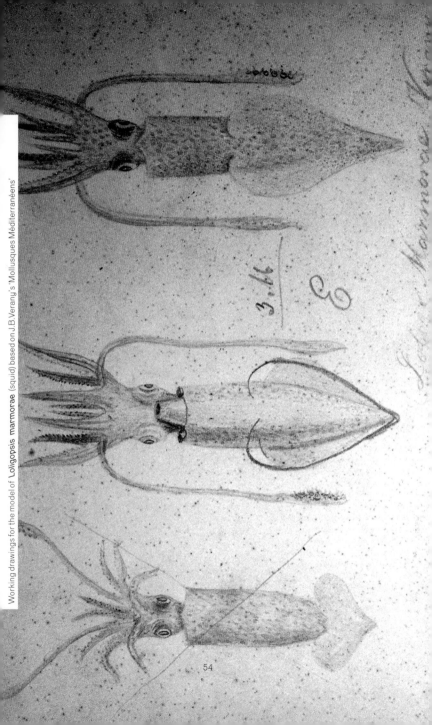

Working drawings for the model of *Loligopsis marmorae* (squid) based on J.B.Verany's 'Mollusques Méditerranéens'

54

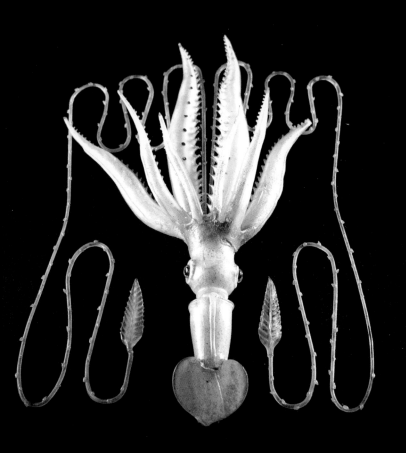

Life-size model of *Loligopsis veranii* (squid) based on J.B.Verany's 'Mollusques Méditerranéens'

Anatomie

von Sepia officinalis: 1, das Verdauungssystem und die Lage ... (Gefässystem blau, Geschlechtssystem grün angedeutet); 2, Gefässystem (... men blau); 3, das Genitalsystem ♂.

1.

Mundmasse
Auge
Untere Speicheldrüse
After
Oesophagus
Leber
Kieme
Darm
Ganglion splanchnicum auf dem Magen.
Gallengang
Tintenbeutel
Magen
Blindsack

Vena cava
Aorta
Kiemenanhänge
Kieme
Vorhof
Vorhof Herz
Kiemenherz nicht Klappen
Kiemenherz

Vesicula seminalis
Testis
Prostata
Vas deferens
♂

56

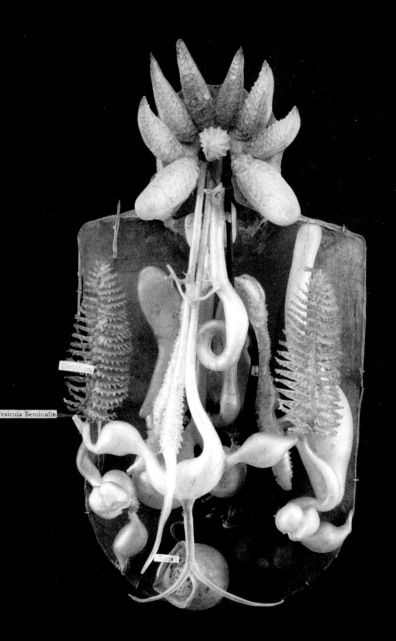

Vesicula Seminalis

Ctenidium

Testis

Anatomical model of **Sepia officinalis** (common cuttlefish)

Cyst

Argonauta argo (octopus) male, two stages

Sycandra raphanus (developmental stage of a sponge)

Ectoderm cells

60

History

1822

On 27 May, Leopold Blaschka, the youngest of three sons, is born into a family of glass and metalworkers in Aicha, Bohemia.

1846

Aged twenty-four Leopold marries Carolina Zimmerman, the daughter of a local mill owner.

1850

Carolina dies in a cholera epidemic.

1852

His father, Joseph Blaschka, dies.

1853

Leopold sets out to visit America. On the voyage he sees jellyfish for the first time and makes studies of them. He stays in New York where he enters into business with several wholesale jewellery firms.

1854

He marries Carolina Riegel and establishes his own workshop in his father-in-law's house.

1857

While working in his father-in-law's business, Leopold begins to model glass tropical flowers from specimens in the greenhouses of Prince de Rohan.

1857

His son Rudolf is born on 17 June.

1860 – 1862

Leopold makes some 100 tropical plants out of glass, mostly orchids mounted on artificial tree stumps.

1863

Leopold moves to Dresden and is introduced by Prince de Rohan to Ludwig Reichenbach, Director of the Natural History Museum and the Botanical Gardens, Dresden, who exhibits the glass flowers in the Gardens' pavilion.

Leopold moves to Dresden. He is asked to make models of sea anemones using the illustrations from 'Actinologia Britannica: A History of the British Sea Anemones and Corals' by the naturalist Philip Henry Gosse, published in 1860.

1864

Leopold experiments with making glass medusae and molluscs.

1866

Ernst Haeckel, zoologist, artist, author and subsequent friend of the Blaschkas, publishes 'Generelle Morphologie'. Among the theories it expounds is that organisms are the product of evolution rather than the result of interacting with their environment. The illustrations are later used as source material by the Blaschkas.

1870

Rudolf begins to study glassworking with his father.

1870s onwards

Leopold's business expands, selling models of jellyfish and siphophores. The sale of glass eyes remains an important source of income.

1871

The Blaschkas' catalogue now lists nearly 300 models, including starfish, sea cucumbers, worms and molluscs. Other sources of income include the production of decorative jewellery and glass eyes for taxidermy and cosmetic uses.

1876

Rudolf joins his father's business full-time.

The South Kensington Museum (now the Natural History Museum) places an order for two complete collections of the invertebrate models.

1877

Leopold orders a selection of preserved marine animals from the zoological station in Naples.
Leopold makes contact with Ernst Haeckel.

1878

Models of the developmental stages of the jellyfish based on Haeckel's work appear in this year's catalogue.

Henry A Ward becomes the Blaschkas' North American agent. The market for models of invertebrates expands and the Blaschkas simplify some of the most popular models in order to streamline production.

1879

Rudolf goes on a field trip to northern Italy and the Adriatic Sea to observe marine animals in their natural habitat.

1880

By 1880 the Blaschkas have installed an aquarium with live specimens in their studio. They order these animals from sources throughout Europe, including the Gulf of Venice and the English Channel.

1885

The workshop produces complex scientific models based on Haeckel's work on embryology.

The number of models offered in the Blaschka catalogue has now grown to over 700.

Mid1880s onwards

Scientists begin to approach the Blaschkas direct to commission specially-made models. These include, in 1885, Professor Franz Schulze who commissions models of sponges based on his research, illustrations and microscope slide samples.

1886 onwards

American Professor George Lincoln Goodale visits the Blaschkas' workshop and requests a series of flowers for the Botanical Museum at Harvard University. Production of these flowers eventually overtakes the production of invertebrates in the Blaschka studio.

1887

Leopold buys a house in Hosterwitz, outside Dresden, and the Blaschkas establish their workshop there.

1890

The Blaschkas are offered a ten-year exclusive contract to produce flower models. Work on the marine models ceases.

1895

Leopold Blaschka dies at the age of 73. Rudolf continues working single-handedly producing the flowers.

1936

Rudolf Blaschka finally ceases work on the glass flowers.

1939

Rudolf Blaschka dies.